To all my friends, especially my fairy friends.

I wish to thank my family for their constant help and support and a special thanks to Gary Kelly Graphic Design and Layout, who made this book possible.

Written & Illustrated by Dolores Keaveney
www.doloreskeaveney.com

Published by Dbee Press
8 New Row, Mullingar, Co.Westmeath, Ireland
Text copyright © Dolores Keaveney 2013
Illustration copyright © Dolores Keaveney 2013
Artwork copyright © Dolores Keaveney 2013
All rights reserved

Printed in Ireland by Castle Print Galway Ltd

Design & Layout by Gary Kelly
Edited by: Aoife Barrett

ISBN 97809571917-2-3

Meet the fairies in my backyard

Some of my best friends are fairies,
They live in my backyard,
Look closely or you will miss them,
Seeing them is quite hard;

I spy them in the mornings
And sometimes late at night,
The sight of the lovely fairies
Just fills me with delight.

Aggie the leafy fairy,
She likes those russet leaves
Which creep along the coal-shed
And rustle in the breeze;

She hangs onto the creeper
Saying: 'Hey guys look at me.'
Her blonde hair blowing wildly
She is feeling very free.

Ells, the pretty fairy,
Loves to visit the rose madder rose,
She gently touches the petals
And tickles them with her toes;

The scent from this beautiful flower
Drifts up to her little nose.
Yes Ells is a pretty fairy
And she loves the rose madder rose.

You'll find **Marr** the butterfly fairy
As she visits the dog-daisy beds,
Fluttering, fluttering, fluttering,
Around the dog-daisy heads;

She soars with the beautiful butterflies,
Flitting and floating so high,
Weaving and dancing freely
Way up in the clear, blue sky.

Kay the lily fairy,
Likes to sit by the lily pond,
Meditating on the healing colours,
She sees far, far beyond;

A rainbow shines out though the mist,
In colours so vibrant and true:
Red, orange, yellow, green,
Indigo, violet and blue.

The fuchsia fairy is Ali,
And she lives in the fuchsia tree.
She swings from the fuchsia branches
And she's as happy as can be;

She sips on the tasty nectar
That she gets from the beautiful flower.
The nectar is like magic,
It gives her a special power.

Moll is a very kind fairy,
Who helps in her positive way,
She sits on a great big toadstool
And gathers her thoughts for the day;

She ponders on who she will visit
What loving and kind words to say.
Yes Moll the kindest fairy
Wonders who she can help each day.

A pretty fairy called Annie,
Lives in the veggie bed,
On the mushrooms, leeks and carrots,
She is careful not to tread;

Courgettes and beans are her favourites
And she eats them every day,
She likes to dress like those veggies,
In her very distinctive way.

Jinni the herbal fairy
Loves to live in the herby patch,
Parsley, sage and rosemary
Are really the perfect catch;

With dandelion, nettle, and cleavers,
Plantain, vetch and dock
She makes a special potion,
That heals you around the clock.

Lu is the artistic fairy,
Who has a big ginger cat;
She dances on the foxgloves,
And wears one as a hat;

Her cat Tommie Ochoa
Is the nicest cat of all.
He likes to walk on the foxglove leaves,
And is careful not to fall.

Kati is the daisy fairy,
She jumps and plays all day
In those big, bright daisy flowers
She whiles the hours away.

She stands upon their big heads,
Kati sits on their green leaves,
Look closely and you will see her;
Be careful not to sneeze!

Mai the pumpkin fairy, hides in the pumpkin patch
And when you stop and pick one, Be sure to really watch;

You'll see her tiny face, just smiling out at you;
As she lies on her little pumpkin, I promise - it's really true.

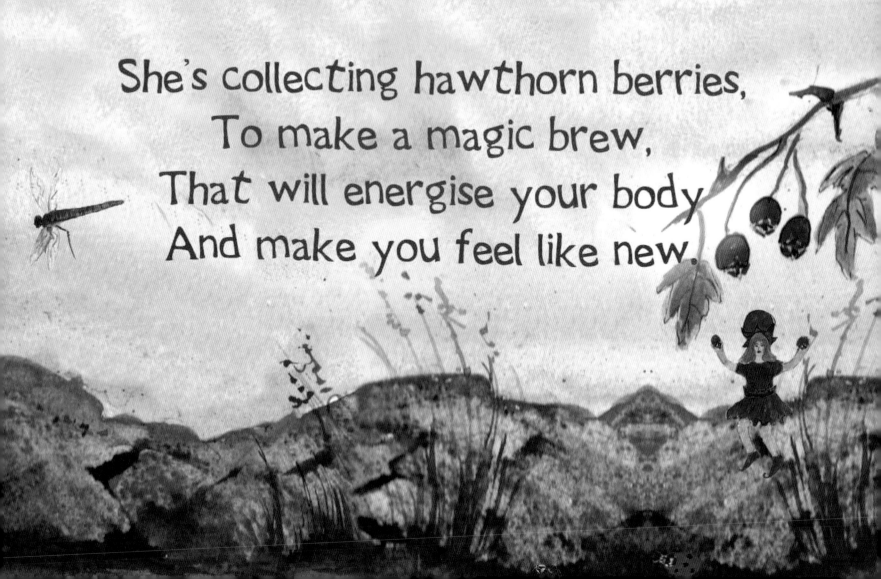

On the bushy hawthorn tree,
Is where you'll surely see
A truly magical fairy,
And her name is **Rosalee**;

She's collecting hawthorn berries,
To make a magic brew,
That will energise your body
And make you feel like new.

There is a poppy fairy,
Whose lovely name is Gail;
If you listen very quietly,
She will tell you a great tale;

The past, present and future,
In her crystal ball she sees,
As she sits on the bright, red poppies,
While they flutter and dance in the breeze.

Lu,

Kati,

Rosalee,

Mai,

Ells,

 Annie,

Jinni,

 Kay,

Marr,

Aggie,

Ali,

Gail

and Moll

"So dear to me
and I love them all.